Level 1 is ideal for
some initial reading
very simply, using a
repeated words.

CM01052412

Special features:

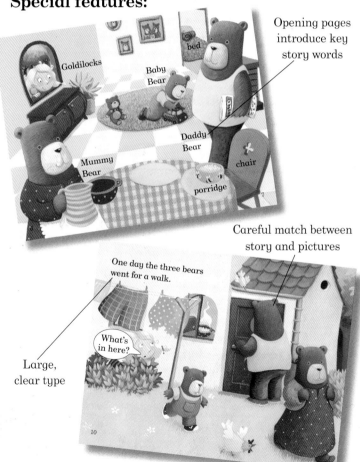

Opening pages
introduce key
story words

Goldilocks

Baby
Bear

bed

Daddy
Bear

Mummy
Bear

chair

porridge

7

Careful match between
story and pictures

One day the three bears
went for a walk.

What's
in here?

Large,
clear type

10

Educational Consultant: Geraldine Taylor
Book Banding Consultant: Kate Ruttle

A catalogue record for this book is available from the British Library

Published by Ladybird Books Ltd
80 Strand, London, WC2R 0RL
A Penguin Company

019
© LADYBIRD BOOKS LTD MMX. This edition MMXIII
Ladybird, Read It Yourself and the Ladybird Logo are registered or
unregistered trade marks of Ladybird Books Limited.

All rights reserved. No part of this publication may be reproduced,
stored in a retrieval system, or transmitted in any form or by any means,
electronic, mechanical, photocopying, recording or otherwise,
without the prior consent of the copyright owner.

ISBN: 978-0-72327-266-3

Printed in China

Goldilocks and the Three Bears

Illustrated by Marina Le Ray

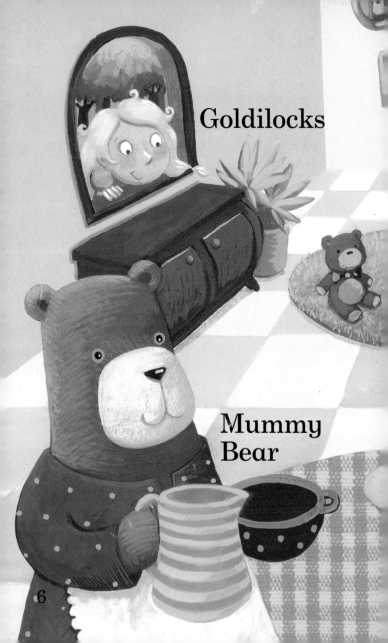

Goldilocks

Mummy
Bear

6

bed

Baby
Bear

Daddy
Bear

chair

porridge

7

Once upon a time
there were three bears.
And the three bears
loved to eat porridge.

9

One day the three bears
went for a walk.

What's in here?

"This porridge is too hot," said Goldilocks.

"This porridge is too cold."

"This porridge is
just right."

Yum,
yum!

"This chair is too hard,"
said Goldilocks.

"This chair is too soft."

"This chair is just right."

Ooops!

"This bed is too hard,"
said Goldilocks.

"This bed is too soft."

"This bed is just right."

Zzzzz...

17

"Who's been eating my porridge?" said Daddy Bear.

"Who's been eating my porridge?" said Mummy Bear.

"My porridge is all gone," said Baby Bear.

"Who's been sitting
in my chair?" said
Daddy Bear.

"Who's been sitting
in my chair?" said
Mummy Bear.

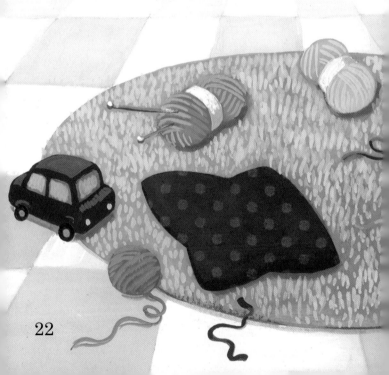

22

"My chair is broken,"
said Baby Bear.

24

"Who's been sleeping in my bed?" said Daddy Bear.

"Who's been sleeping in my bed?" said Mummy Bear.

"Who is sleeping in
my bed?" said Baby Bear.

"Time to go!"
said Goldilocks.

How much do you remember about the story of Goldilocks and the Three Bears? Answer these questions and find out!

- What is wrong with the first chair Goldilocks tries?

- Whose porridge is just right?

- Where do the three bears find Goldilocks?